Contents

Meet the Mystery Mob

Name:

Gummy

FYI: Gummy hasn't got much brain – and even fewer teeth.

Loves: Soup.

Hates: Toffee chews.

Fact: The brightest thing about him is his shirt.

Name:

Lee

FYI: If Lee was any cooler he'd be a cucumber.

Loves: Hip-hop.

Hates: Hopscotch.

Fact: He has his own designer label (which he peeled off a tin).

Name:

Rob

FYI: Rob lives in his own world – he's just visiting planet Earth.

Loves: Daydreaming.

Hates: Nightmares.

Fact: Rob always does his homework – he just forgets to write it down.

Name:

Dwayne

FYI: Dwayne is smarter than a tree full of owls.

Loves: Anything complicated.

Hates: Join-the-dots books.

Fact: If he was any brighter you could use him as a floodlight at football matches.

Name:

Chet

FYI: Chet is as brave as a lion with steel jaws.

Loves: Having adventures.

Hates: Knitting.

Fact: He's as tough as the chicken his granny cooks for his tea.

Name:

Adi

FYI: Adi is as happy as a football fan with tickets to the big match.

Loves: Telling jokes.

Hates: Moaning minnies.

Fact: He knows more jokes than a jumbo joke book.

Do-you-think-he-saurus?

The Mystery Mob are at their local park,
where there are life-sized models
of dinosaurs. Dwayne knows all about
dinosaurs. He tells the others so many
facts that they nickname him
Dwayne-a-bore-us.

Rob, Lee, Chet and Adi get so fed up
with him that they slip off while
he is telling Gummy all about
the eating habits of the Greedyosaurus.

Dwayne The Greedyosaurus ate everything it could get its teeth on. It was always hungry.

Gummy I like the sound of the Greedyosaurus.

Dwayne That's because it reminds you of you.

Gummy Huh! I'm not greedy. I just have a big appetite.

Dwayne Yes, your appetite's so big it's worn your front teeth away.

Gummy No! They fell out when I bit into a bumper bar of extra-chewy toffee. And that's the tooth, the whole tooth and nothing but the tooth.

Dwayne I told you not to eat that toffee. I said it would get you into a sticky situation.

Gummy Whatever! Hey, where have the others gone?

Dwayne I don't know. They've vanished. Just like your front teeth.

Gummy Stop going on about my teeth!

Dwayne Sorry, Gum, I get the 'filling'
I'm upsetting you!

Gummy Doh! You're getting as bad as Adi.
He's always making silly jokes.

Dwayne You're right. I don't do jokes.
I do facts. Now, let me tell you
some more.

Gummy Okay. Is it a fact that dinosaurs
are extinct?

Dwayne It is.

Gummy Then how come there are two
sitting on that rock over there,
looking at us?

Dwayne Come on, Gummy, I'm not
falling for that!

Gummy I'm not kidding you.
They're sitting there as large
as life. Well, a bit smaller
than life, I guess, 'cos they look
like baby dinos to me.

Dwayne Oh yeah, Gummy ... No way!
You're right!

Dwayne is amazed to see two
tiny T-Rex running past him.
They go into the long grass.
The boys chase after them.

Ice-cream Age

Gummy Can you see those dinosaurs, Dwayne?

Dwayne Yes! They're over by that ice-cream van.

Gummy Maybe they're going to get a vanilla cone with a chocolate flake.

Dwayne I don't think so, Gum.

Gummy Why not?

Dwayne They haven't got any money!

Gummy That won't stop a T-Rex. They take what they want. Even little guys like these two.

Dwayne We've got to catch them and find out where they've come from.

Gummy How are we going to do that?

Dwayne We can use this rubbish bin to trap them.

Gummy How? They're dinos, not litter louts.

Dwayne We'll sneak up behind them and drop the bin over their heads.

Gummy Gotcha! Let's do it.

The two dinos scramble up on the serving
hatch of the van. The ice-cream man
is reading the paper. He doesn't notice
them. Then Dwayne and Gummy race up
with the bin. The dinos see Dwayne
and Gummy.

Dwayne Okay, Gum, it's slam-dunk time!

The dinos dive back out of the van.
Dwayne and Gummy miss! Litter flies
everywhere.

Man   Hey, you've dumped rubbish all over my van!

Gummy   Sorry, but we're trying to catch two dinosaurs.

Dwayne   Did you see them?

Man   (angrily) No, I did not! Get out of it, or I'll phone the police!

Gummy   Err … Can I have a '99' before you call 999?

Man   Grrrrr!!!!!

Dwayne   Now you've done it!

The two boys run off. The ice-cream man shakes his fist at them.

Gummy   Phew! That was a narrow escape.

Dwayne   Yes. But we should have stayed and cleared up the mess we made.

Gummy   Yeah, but we've got two dinos to track down.

Dwayne   You're right. We'd better find those T-Rex – fast.

Men in Black

Suddenly Dwayne grabs Gummy's arm
and pulls him behind a tree.

Gummy   Hey, what's up?

Dwayne   Look over there! We're not
            the only ones after those dinos.

Dwayne points at two men in black
combat gear and helmets with tinted
visors, creeping up on the two T-Rex.

17

The tiny dinosaurs snap and snarl
at the two men but they snatch them
and pop them into a large sack.

Gummy Who are those guys?

Dwayne I don't know, and I don't think
they'd tell us even if we
asked them.

Gummy So what are we going to do?

Dwayne We're going to follow them
and find out what they're up to.

The men in black head off
out of the park. Dwayne and Gummy
track them as they walk swiftly
through the streets.

Gummy   Oh no, they've stopped
            outside the gates of that
            spooky old mansion.

One of the men speaks at an intercom
set in the wall. The gates swing open
and the men hurry on up the driveway.
The gates swing shut behind them.

Dwayne Rats! We can't follow them now.

Gummy Yes, we can. We'll climb over
the wall.

Gummy scrambles up on to the top
of the wall. Dwayne doesn't find it so easy.

Dwayne Hey, Gummy, I need some
help here. Give me a hand.

Gummy reaches down and tries to drag
Dwayne up behind him.

Gummy Blimey, Dwayne, you weigh
a ton.

Dwayne Whoa, Gummy. You're pulling my
arm out of its socket.

Gummy Oh, stop moaning. Just one
more tug and you'll be up.

But Gummy pulls too hard. They both fall
backwards off the top of the wall
and crash land in a bush in the garden.

21

Dwayne You idiot!

Gummy Sorry! I guess I just don't know my own strength. Anyway, this bush is handy for spying on those guys.

Dwayne True. Hey, they're handing the bag over to someone.

Dwayne Who is it?

Gummy I can't see. They're standing in the shadows.

The mystery figure hands the two men
a thick roll of money and then goes back
into the mansion with the sack.

Dwayne Watch out! The men in black
are coming back.

The boys duck back behind the bush.
The two men stride past them.
They are too busy counting their money
to notice Dwayne and Gummy.

Gummy Phew, that's was a close call.

Dwayne Yeah, but now we're going to make a house call.

Gummy What do you mean?

Dwayne We're going to break into the mansion and find out what's going on!

Getting in a Flap

The boys creep
round to the back of the mansion.

Gummy It's hopeless. We'll never find
a way in. We're not burglars.

Dwayne Look, there's a dog flap in that
door. We'll crawl in through that.

Gummy You're barking mad, Dwayne.

Dwayne No, I'm not, come on!

The boys squeeze through the dog flap.
They find themselves in a large creepy
room. It is filled with stuffed animals.

Gummy Yikes! This room looks like
it belongs to a crazy collector.

Dwayne Yeah, someone who collects rare
creatures – like the two dinos.

Gummy Dinos aren't rare –
they're extinct.

The door to the room opens and a tall
thin man walks in. He is holding a cage
with the two tiny T-Rex in it. He looks
at the boys and his mouth twists into
a cruel smile.

Max   No, dinosaurs aren't extinct –
but they will be as soon as I
add these two to my collection.

Dwayne You're mad!

Max   No, I'm Max Megabucks –
the world's most evil man.
I heard that some inventor
had found two frozen dinosaur
eggs at the North Pole. So I had
my men steal them from him
and bring them to me.

Gummy   And then you thawed the eggs
and hatched them.

Max   Yes. But the T-Rex escaped.

Dwayne Good for them.

Max   But I've got them back now.
And I've also got you. I think
I'll add you to my collection
as well!

Gummy Arrrghhh! We're done for!

Max   Oh yes, I'm afraid you are.
But I'm too busy to deal with you
at the moment. So I'm going to
lock you in here for now.
But I'll be back soon.

Max chuckles nastily. Then he puts
the cage down and goes out of the room,
locking the door behind him.

Dwayne I don't know why he's laughing.
He forgot to ask us how we got
in here.

Gummy It doesn't matter. He's locked
the door.

Dwayne Yes, but we came in through
the dog flap.

Gummy Yay! So we can go out
the same way.

Dwayne Exactly. Now grab
that dino cage,
Gum, and let's go!

Out of Time

The boys
scramble out of the flap,
but they are in for
a big surprise. Max Megabucks
is waiting for them with the men in black.

Max   Ha! Ha! I may be evil, but I do
love a little joke.

Gummy So you knew about the dog flap
all along.

Max   He! He! Of course I did.
Now get back inside.

Dwayne Hang on. Why's the ground shaking?

Gummy It sounds like an angry elephant.

Dwayne No, it's an angry T-Rex, and it's charging right at us!

A large T-Rex races across the garden. There's a man chasing after it. Gummy and Dwayne dive headfirst back through the dog flap.

Max's men run for it and scramble over
the wall. But the T-Rex bites Max's bottom
before he can escape. She dangles Max
in the air. Her jaws are clamped
on the seat of his trousers.

Max   Help! Save me!

Dwayne and Gummy crawl back out
into the garden. They have the dino cage
with them.

Gummy Where did that T-Rex come from?

Dwayne Search me.

Just then, the man who was chasing
the T-Rex runs up to them.
It's Dwayne's uncle, the inventor!

Dwayne Hey, Uncle! What are you
doing here?

Uncle I'm tracking down the man
who stole the dinosaur eggs.
But I see you've beaten me to it.
Well done, guys. I'll take those
little T-Rex now.

Gummy Okay, but what about the big
T-Rex?

Uncle That's Tina. She's their mum.
She's been going crazy ever since
her frozen eggs were stolen
from my lab.

Dwayne So *you* were the inventor who found the eggs. But where did you find Tina?

Uncle She was frozen at the North Pole as well. I mean, who did you think laid the eggs in the first place?

Gummy But she's well scary.

Uncle No, she's just a worried mum. She'll be fine now she's got her boys back.

Dwayne   So what are you going to do
with them?

Uncle   I'll take them all back to the past
in my Time Machine and set
them free.

Gummy   Great. But what are we going
to do with Max Megabucks?

Dwayne   Well, I think he's fed up with just
hanging about. So why don't we
rescue him from Tina – then
hand him over to the police?

Gummy   Great idea. Hey, do you know
what dinosaur police were called?

Dwayne   No. What were they called?

Gummy   Triceracops!

Dwayne and Uncle

Doh!

About the author

Roger Hurn has:

 had a hit record in Turkey

 won *The Weakest Link* on TV

swum with sharks on the
Great Barrier Reef.

Now he's a writer, and he hopes you like
reading about the Mystery Mob as much as he
likes writing about them.

The dinosaur quiz

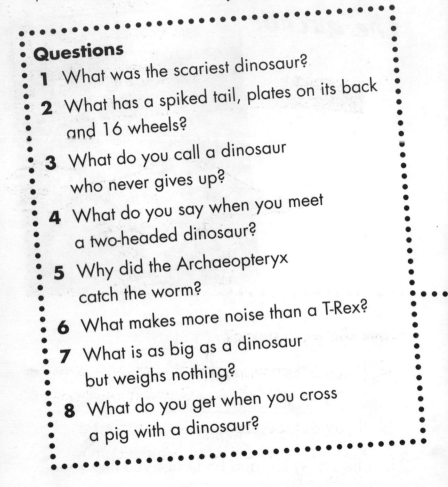

Questions

1 What was the scariest dinosaur?

2 What has a spiked tail, plates on its back and 16 wheels?

3 What do you call a dinosaur who never gives up?

4 What do you say when you meet a two-headed dinosaur?

5 Why did the Archaeopteryx catch the worm?

6 What makes more noise than a T-Rex?

7 What is as big as a dinosaur but weighs nothing?

8 What do you get when you cross a pig with a dinosaur?

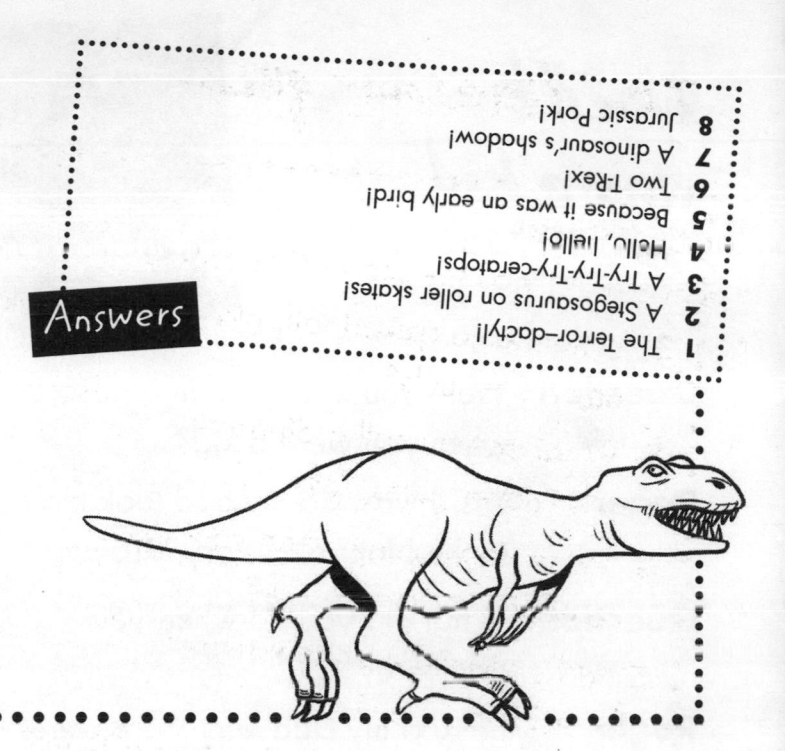

How did you score?

🖐 If you got all eight dinosaur answers correct, then you are definitely Quizosaurus Rex!

🖐 If you got six dinosaur answers correct, then you're no dinosaur when it comes to quizzes.

🖐 If you got fewer than four dinosaur answers correct, then you're in danger of becoming a fossil!

41

When I was a kid

Question Were you interested in dinosaurs
when you were a kid?

Roger Yes, I was. So my dad took me
to the Natural History Museum.

Question What did you do when you
got there?

Roger I asked my Dad why there were
so many old bones in the museum.

Question And what did he say?

Roger He said it was because they couldn't
afford to buy any new ones.

Question What was your favourite dinosaur?

Roger Well, I liked the kind of dinosaurs
that could jump higher than a house.

Question Really? Which dinosaurs were they?

Roger All of them. Houses can't jump.

Adi's favourite dinosaur joke

What weighs two tons and sticks to the roof of your mouth?

A peanut butter and dinosaur sandwich!

How to be a dinosaur hunter

 Some scientists think that birds are descended from dinosaurs. So throw some bird seed in your garden, and you'll see lots of feathered 'dinosaurs'.

 If you want to hunt for a real dinosaur you'll need a time machine – the last dinosaur died 65 million years ago.

 If you haven't got a time machine, you can still hunt for fossils from the time of the dinosaurs. The best place to hunt for dinosaur fossils is in a museum.

 Fossils are like a window into the past. But if a T-Rex sticks his head through the window – run!

 If you find some new bones in your garden, don't too get excited – your dog probably buried them! Dinosaur bones are old.

 If you want to find your own dinosaur fossils, go to places where fossils come to the surface – like a ploughed field or a beach.

 Never go fossil hunting on your own or where it's unsafe. It's not that the dinosaurs will get you, but fossils can be found in hard-to-get-to places.

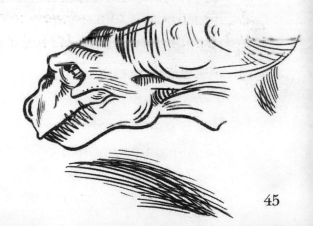

Five fantastic facts about dinosaurs

1   The first dinosaurs appeared on Earth 230 million years ago.

2   The last dinosaurs died out 65 million years before the first people appeared on the Earth. So, this means *The Flintstones* is NOT a history programme.

3   The Troodon was the smartest dinosaur. It looked like a bird and had a big brain in a small body. It couldn't do sums or read and write, but it was an excellent hunter!

4   Most types of dinosaurs ate plants – not other dinosaurs. Hmmm ... maybe someone should try telling that to Tyrannosaurus Rex!

5   The heaviest dinosaur was Brachiosaurus. It weighed 80 tonnes. This is as much as 17 African elephants!

Dinosaur lingo

Dinosaur In Greek, 'deinos' means 'fearfully great' and 'saurus' means 'lizard'. So a dinosaur is a 'fearfully great lizard'.

Extinct This means no longer existing. Dinosaurs became extinct more than 65 million years ago. Luckily for humans!

Fossils Fossils are the remains, or evidence, of plants or animals that lived a long time ago. Your teachers may be old, but they are NOT fossils!

Palaeontologist This is the name of the type of scientist who studies dinosaurs and other fossils. Dwayne wants to be a palaeontologist. The rest of the Mystery Mob think he is already a bit of a fossil.

ROAROAROAR! The sound an angry T-Rex makes. Let's hope you only read it and never hear it!

Mystery Mob

Mystery Mob Set 1:

Mystery Mob and the Abominable Snowman
Mystery Mob and the Big Match
Mystery Mob and the Circus of Doom
Mystery Mob and the Creepy Castle
Mystery Mob and the Haunted Attic
Mystery Mob and the Hidden Treasure
Mystery Mob and the Magic Bottle
Mystery Mob and the Missing Millions
Mystery Mob and the Monster on the Moor
Mystery Mob and the Mummy's Curse
Mystery Mob and the Time Machine
Mystery Mob and the UFO

Mystery Mob Set 2:

Mystery Mob and the Ghost Town
Mystery Mob and the Bonfire Night Plot
Mystery Mob and the April Fools' Day Joker
Mystery Mob and the Great Pancake Day Race
Mystery Mob and the Scary Santa
Mystery Mob and the Conker Conspiracy
Mystery Mob and the Top Talent Contest
Mystery Mob and the Night in the Waxworks
Mystery Mob and the Runaway Train
Mystery Mob and the Wrong Robot
Mystery Mob and the Day of the Dinosaurs
Mystery Mob and the Man-eating Tiger

RISING ★ STARS

Mystery Mob
and the
Haunted Attic

Roger Hurn

700031878915

RISING★STARS

Rising Stars UK Ltd.
22 Grafton Street, London W1S 4EX
www.risingstars-uk.com

The right of Roger Hurn to be identified as the author of this work
has been asserted by him in accordance with the Copyright, Design
and Patents Act 1988.

Published 2007

Text, design and layout © Rising Stars UK Ltd.

Cover design: Button plc
Illustrator: Stik, Bill Greenhead for Illustration
Text design and typesetting: Andy Wilson
Publisher: Gill Budgell
Publishing manager: Sasha Morton
Editor: Catherine Baker
Series consultant: Cliff Moon

British Library Cataloguing in Publication Data.
A CIP record for this book is available from the British Library

ISBN: 978-1-84680-218-8

Printed in the UK by CPI Bookmarque, Croydon, CR0 4TD

FSC

Mixed Sources
Product group from well-managed
forests and other controlled sources
www.fsc.org Cert no. TT-COC-002227
© 1996 Forest Stewardship Council